Hug Your Children

Written by

Kevin Kitrell Ross

Books may be purchased in quantity and/or special sales by
contacting the publisher.

Mynd Matters Publishing
715 Peachtree Street NE
Suites 100 & 200
Atlanta, GA 30308
www.myndmatterspublishing.com

Pb ISBN - 978-1-953307-89-7
HD ISBN - 978-1-953307-90-3

FIRST EDITION

To the many hugging arms that have held me and mine through the years,
To the ones that saw us through our wildest joys and greatest fears,
Your presence in our lives has given us a soft place to fall,
And whatever way you were there, we love you one and all.

—Your Ross Family

This Rev. Kev Rhyming Reader is especially dedicated to "Grandma Gigi,"
Mrs. Eula Eikerenkoetter, for all the hugs, love, and magical moments we
have shared together and will continue to create for years to come.

Hug your children while they're young.
Hug them every day.

4

Hold them tight and don't let go.
Hug them as they play.

5

Hug your children when they're brave.
Hug them when they're shy.

Hug your children when they're afraid.
Hug them when they cry.

Hug your children when they're mean.
Hug them when they lie.

Hug them as they make pretend.
Hug them when they spy.

Hug them when they make mistakes.
Hug them when they're right.

10

Hug them when they clean their plates.

Hug them every night.

Hug your children,
big and small.

13

Hug them for the world.
Hug your children, short and tall.
Hug them, boy and girl.

14

Hug your children when they're at home.
Hug them while at school.

Hug your children everywhere.
Let hugging be your rule.

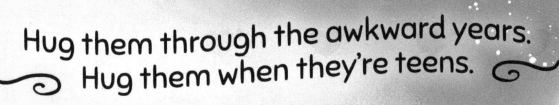

Hug them through the awkward years.
Hug them when they're teens.

17

Hug them as they run and play.
Hug them in between.

18

Take them to your heart just now.
Do it quickly, please.

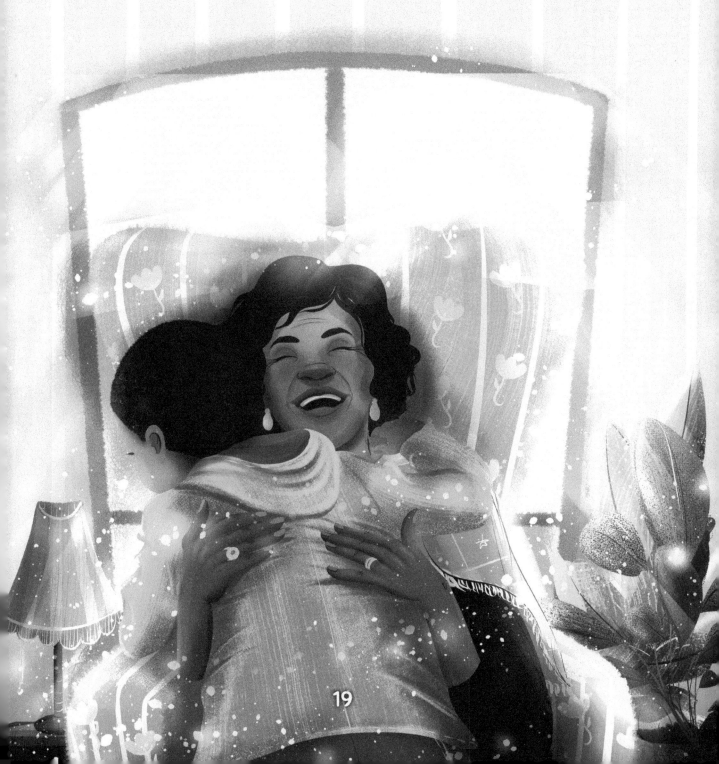

Hug your children when you're awake.
Hug them in your dreams.

Hug them now for goodness sake.
Start your own hug team.

Hug them on the holidays.
Hug them as you work.

Let hugging them be the greatest gift
they could ever get on Earth.

Hug them for the lonely years, when
time and space have come,

when you can no longer wipe their tears
or hear them having fun.

Hug them now before it's too late.
Show them that you care.

Make them hugging millionaires, with
hugs and love to spare!

9 781953 307903